D1107571

A Little Book of
OLD RHYMES

Collected and Illustrated by
CICELY MARY BARKER

Blackie & Son Ltd Glasgow and London
The Two Continents Publishing Group
New York

Many of the rhymes in this book are taken, with
permission, from Mr G. F. Northall's book
English Folk Rhymes.

Text and illustrations copyright

© 1936 Blackie & Son Limited

ISBN 0 216 90101 4 (U.K. cased)
ISBN 0 216 90291 6 (paperback)
ISBN 0 8467 0257 6 (U.S.A.)

This edition published 1976

Blackie & Son Limited
Bishopbriggs, Glasgow G64 2NZ
450/452 Edgware Road, London W2 1EG

The Two Continents Publishing Group
30 East 42 Street, New York, New York 10017

Printed in Great Britain by
Robert MacLehose and Company Limited
Printers to the University of Glasgow

TINGLE~.
TANGLE
TITMOUSE

Come hither, little piggy-wig,
Come and learn your letters,
And you shall have a knife and fork
To eat with, like your betters.
" Oh no," the little pig replied,
" My trough will do as well;
I'd rather eat my victuals there
Than learn to read and spell."

With a tingle-tangle titmouse,
  Robin knows great A,
B and C and D and E,
  F, G, H, I, J, K.

Come hither, little pussy-cat;
If you will grammar study,
I'll give you silver clogs to wear
Whene'er the weather's muddy.
" Oh, if I grammar learn," said Puss,
" Your house will in a trice
Be overrun from top to bottom
With the rats and mice."

With a tingle-tangle titmouse,
Robin knows great A,
B and C and D and E,
F, G, H, I, J, K.

Come hither, little puppy-dog;
I'll give you a new collar
If you will learn to read and spell
And be a clever scholar.
" Oh no," the little dog replied,
" I've other fish to fry,
For I must learn to guard the house
And bark when thieves are nigh."

With a tingle-tangle titmouse,
Robin knows great A,
B and C and D and E,
F, G, H, I, J, K.

Come hither then, good little boy,
And learn your alphabet,
And you a pair of boots and spurs
Like your papa shall get.
" Oh yes, I'll learn my alphabet;
And when I well can read,
My kind papa has promised me
A little long-tailed steed.''

With a tingle-tangle titmouse,
  Robin knows great A,
B and C and D and E,
  F, G, H, I, J, K.

"And you shall have a knife and fork
To eat with like your betters."

BARLEY BRIDGE
A SINGING GAME

Q. How many miles to Barley Bridge?
A. *Fourscore miles and ten!*
Q. Shall we be there by candle-light?
A. *Yes, and back again;*
   If your heels are nimble and light,
   You may get there by candle-light.
Q. Open the gates as wide as wide,
   And let King George go through with his bride!
   A curtsey to you, and a curtsey to you,
   If you please, will you let the king's horses go
   through?

A Begging Rhyme.

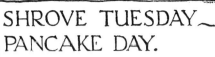

Knick a knock upon the block;
Flour and lard is very dear,
Please we come a-shroving here.
Your pan's hot and my pan's cold,
Hunger makes us shrovers bold:
Please to give poor shrovers something here.

Mothering Sunday

Simnel Sunday—Mid Lent

On Mothering Sunday, above all other,
Every child should dine with its mother.

NOTE.—A Simnel Cake is the proper present for a daughter
to bring her mother on this Sunday.

The Deaf Old Woman

" Old woman, old woman, wilt thee go a-shearin'?"
" Speak a little louder, sir, I'm very hard of hearin'."

" Old woman, old woman, wilt thee go a-gleanin'?"
" Speak a little louder, I canna tell the meanin'!"

" Old woman, old woman, wilt thee go a-walkin'?"
" Speak a little louder, or what's the use o' talkin'!"

" Old woman, old woman, shall I kiss thee dearly?"
" Thank you, kind sir, I hear you very clearly!"

The Merchants of London

Hey diddle dinkety, poppety, pet,
The Merchants of London they wear scarlét,
Silk in the collar, and gold on the hem,
So merrily march the merchantmen.

"Speak a little louder, Sir, I'm very hard of hearin'."

LAVENDER'S BLUE.

Lavender's blue, diddle diddle, lavender's green,
When I am king, diddle diddle, you shall be queen.

Who told you so, diddle diddle, who told you so?
'Twas my own heart, diddle diddle, that told me so.

Call up your men, diddle diddle, set them to work,
Some with a rake, diddle diddle, some with a fork,

Some to make hay, diddle diddle, some to thresh corn,
Whilst you and I, diddle diddle, keep ourselves warm.

For Moonlight Nights

I see the moon, the moon sees me;
God bless the sailors on the sea.

A New Year's Rhyme

Wassail, wassail, to our town,
The cup is white, the ale is brown;
The cup is made of the ashen tree,
And so is your ale of the good barley.
Little maid, little maid, turn the pin,
Open the door and let us come in.
God be here, God be there,
I wish you all a happy New Year.

NOTE.—The Wassail Cup was a wooden cup (one rhyme says " made of the rosemary tree ") of spiced ale, apples, and sugar, which they drank at the New Year. The word Wassail comes from the Anglo-Saxon Wæs hâl! be whole!—that is to say, good health to you! Children carried round a bunch of evergreens hung with apples, oranges, and ribbons, called a Wessel-bob. " Turn the pin " means " unfasten the latch ".

The Wassail Song

Here we come a-wassailing
Among the leaves so green;
Here we come a-wandering,
So fair to be seen:
Love and joy come to you,
And to you your wassail too,
And God bless you and send you
A happy New Year.

We are not daily beggars
That beg from door to door,
But we are neighbours' children,
Whom you have seen before.

The roads are very dirty,
Our shoes are very thin;
We've got a little pocket
To put a penny in.

God bless the master of this house,
Likewise the mistress too,
And all the little children,
That round the table go.

Good Master and Mistress,
While you're sitting by the fire,
Pray think of us poor children
Who are wandering in the mire.
Love and joy come to you,
And to you your wassail too,
And God bless you and send you
    A happy New Year.

Wassail, wassail, to our town —

The Bells

I

Pancakes and fritters,
Say the bells of St. Peter's.
Where must we fry 'em?
Say the bells of Cold Higham.
In yonder land furrow,
Say the bells of Wellingborough.
You owe me a shilling,
Say the bells of Great Billing.
When will you pay me?
Say the bells of Middleton Cheney.
When I am able,
Say the bells of Dunstable.
That will never be,
Say the bells of Coventry.
O yes it will,
Says Northampton great bell.

Three crows on a tree,
Say the bells of Oswestry.

Roast beef, and be merry,
Say the bells of Shrewsbury.

Three gold canaries,
Say the bells of St. Mary's.

A boiling pot and a stewing pan,
Say the bells of St. Julian.

You're a rogue for sartin,
Say the bells of St. Martin.

Ivy, holly, and mistletoe,
Say the bells of Wistanstow.

The Cuckoo

The cuckoo's a bonny bird, he whistles as he flies,
He brings us good tidings, he tells us no lies;
He drinks the cold water to make his voice clear,
And when he sings cuckoo the summer is near;
Sings cuckoo in April, cuckoo in May,
Cuckoo in June, and then flies away.

The Bat

Airymouse, Airymouse, fly over my head,
And you shall have a crust o' bread;
And when I brew and when I bake,
You shall have a piece of my wedding-cake.

"Airymouse, Airymouse, fly over my head —"

A May Day Rhyme

Good morning, Missus and Master,
  I wish you a happy day;
Please to smell my garland,
  Because it's the first of May.

The Mayers' Song

We've been a-rambling all this night,
  And sometime of this day;
And now returning back again
  We bring a branch of May.

A branch of May we bring you here,
  And at your door it stands;
It is a sprout well budded out,
  The work of the Lord's hands.

The hedges and trees they are so green,
  As green as any leek;
Our Heavenly Father, He watered them
  With His heavenly dew so sweet.

The heavenly gates are open wide,
  Our paths are beaten plain;
And if a man be not too far gone,
  He may return again.

So dear, so dear as Christ loved us,
  And for our sins was slain,
Christ bids us turn from wickedness
  Back to the Lord again.

The moon shines bright, the stars give a light,
  A little before it is day,
So God bless you all, both great and small,
  And send you a joyful May.

NOTE.—Nowadays we do not usually find much may in blossom on the 1st of May; this is because the calendar was altered in 1752, and we begin the year earlier than they did before that date—something like the way in which the clocks are put back for Summer Time. Old May Day was what we now call the 13th May, when plenty of may is out; and, you see, these songs belong to the old days before the calendar was altered.

" And now returning back again,
    We bring a branch of May."

A PAIL OF WATER.

A Singing Game

Draw a pail of water
For my lady's daughter;
My father's a king, and my mother's a queen,
My two little sisters are dressed in green,
Stamping grass and parsley,
Marigold leaves and daisies.
One rush, two rush,
Prythee, fine lady, come under my bush.

The Wren

In the greenhouse lives a wren,
Little friend of little men;
When they're good she tells them where
To find the apple, quince, and pear.

A Devonshire Knee-verse

Come up, my horse, to Bundleigh fair;
What shall we have when we come there?
Sugar and figs and elecampane;
Home again, home again, Master and Dame.

Counting

One, two, three, four,
Mary at the cottage door,
Eating cherries off a plate,
Five, six, seven, eight.

Cherry Stones

Tinker, tailor,
Soldier, sailor,
Rich man, poor man,
Gentleman, farmer,
Apothecary,
Ploughboy,
Thief.

About the Bush

About the bush, Willie,
  About the bee-hive,
About the bush, Willie,
  I'll meet thee alive.

Then to my ten shillings
  Add you but a groat,
I'll go to Newcastle
  And buy a new coat.

Five and five shillings,
  Five and a crown;
Five and five shillings
  Will buy a new gown.

Five and five shillings,
  Five and a groat;
Five and five shillings
  Will buy a new coat.

"Then to my ten shillings
            Add you but a groat."

ST. CLEMENT'S DAY _ 23rd November.

Clemany! Clemany! Clemany mine!
A good red apple, a pint of wine,
Some of your mutton and some of your veal,
If it is good, pray give me a deal.
An apple, a pear, a plum or a cherry,
Any good thing to make us merry;
A bouncing buck and a velvet chair,
Clemany comes but once a year.
Off with the pot and on with the pan;
A good red apple, and I'll be gone.

THE BIRDS

A SUSSEX RHYME

Robins and wrens
Are God Almighty's friends;
Martins and swallows
Are God Almighty's scholars.

(I am afraid you must say " swallers ", to make this rhyme!)

A WARNING

The robin and the redbreast,
The robin and the wren,
If ye take from their nest,
Ye'll never thrive again.

The robin and the redbreast,
The martin and the swallow,
If ye touch one of their eggs,
Bad luck will surely follow.

TWO HUSHABYES

I

Hush-a-bye, baby,
Nurse is away,
Sisters and brothers are gone out to play;
But I by your cradle,
Dear baby, will keep,
To guard you from danger and sing you to sleep.

II

Hush-a-bye, baby,
Pussy's a lady,
Mousie has gone to the mill;
And if you don't cry
She'll come back by and by,
So hush-a-bye, baby, lie still.

"But I by your cradle, dear baby, will keep."